Aliza in MitzvahLand

By Bracha Goetz

Illustrated by Yishia Suval

The Judaica Press, Inc.

Aliza in MitzvahLand

© 2009 Bracha Goetz

ISBN: 978-1-60763-008-1

Editor: Nachum Shapiro
Illustrator: Yishia Suval
Cover illustration: R. Jennings

THE JUDAICA PRESS, INC.
123 Ditmas Avenue / Brooklyn, NY 11218
718-972-6200 / 800-972-6201
info@judaicapress.com
www.judaicapress.com

Printed in Mexico

On a cold, rainy day,
In a house on a hill,
A little girl sat
At her window sill.

Her name was Aliza
And she sat there so sadly.
She had nothing to do,
And she really felt badly.

So she went to her mirror
And made grouchy faces.
She wished she could be
In happier places.

She complained to the girl
In the mirror right there,
"I have nothing to do,
AND IT JUST ISN'T FAIR!"

4

But she looked so funny,
Whining like that,
That the girl in the mirror
Started laughing right back!

The mirror-girl giggled.
"Nothing to do?
You're seeing things backwards ...
I'll prove it to you!"

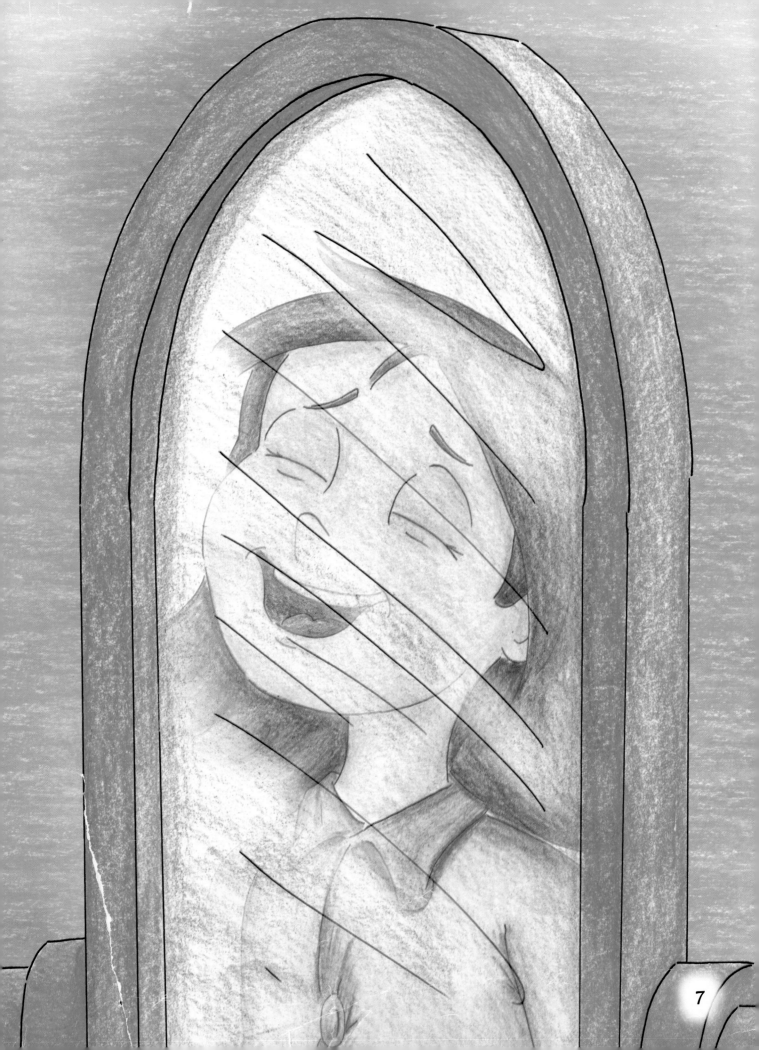

"Step into my world!"
The mirror-girl said,
And Aliza wondered,
"Is this all in my head?"

Then she felt a strong tug,
And she let out a shout,
And the whole world just flipped
Completely inside-out!

She soon found herself sitting
In a huge field of green.
"Where am I?" she said.
"What does this all mean?"

She gazed 'round in wonder,
Her eyes big and blue,
At the looking-glass world
She had fallen into!

"MitzvahLand," a sign said,
Showing the way,
So she hurried along
Without delay.

She went on inside
And was greeted with cheer:
"Hello, Miss Aliza,
We are so glad you're here!

"You've got nothing to do?
Come join us! Lend a hand!"
Said the Welcome Committee
In MitzvahLand.

MITZ

Welcome

"...tep right inside
...' look all around!"
...iza went in
...ere's what she found ...

A world filled with mitzvos
Wherever she turned.
There were mitzvos all over,
She suddenly learned.

Wherever she walked
She was greeted with smiles.
The kids were all friendly
For miles and miles.

"St
And
So Al
And he

Children were jumping up!
Were they getting treats?
No! They were just so happy
To give elders their seats!

17

And these smiling children
Were showing they cared.
Just look at their faces
And see how they shared!

19

They went looking for mitzvos
Even when it rained.
No one was kvetching
And no one complained.

21

Seeing so much to do,
Aliza felt a bit dizzy.
Everyone, chasing mitzvahs,
Looked so happy and busy!

Said Aliza, "This place
Is where I like to be -
A world where mitzvah chances
Are all that I see!

"There's not one grouchy face,
On even one child ...
Hey! My frown's gone, too!"
She said as she smiled.

23

"Wait! Is *this* world backwards,
Or did I have it all wrong?
Could it be that I've seen things
Backwards all along?

"When I've got nothing to do,
It's because I'm forgetting ...
Our world was made for giving,
Not getting!

"There's always something to do!
Flipped around now, I see!
There is always a mitzvah
Just waiting for me!

"So when I sit in my room
Crying, 'I've got nothing to do!'
That's the perfect time
For a big switcheroo!"

As soon as she said that,
Aliza felt something change.
She found herself on her bedroom floor.
"Well, *that* was quite strange!

What happened? Where am I?
Was I dreaming?" she said.
"Was this whole adventure
Really just in my head?

"Well, why am I sitting here,
When there's so much to do?
There are so many mitzvos
For me." And you, too!

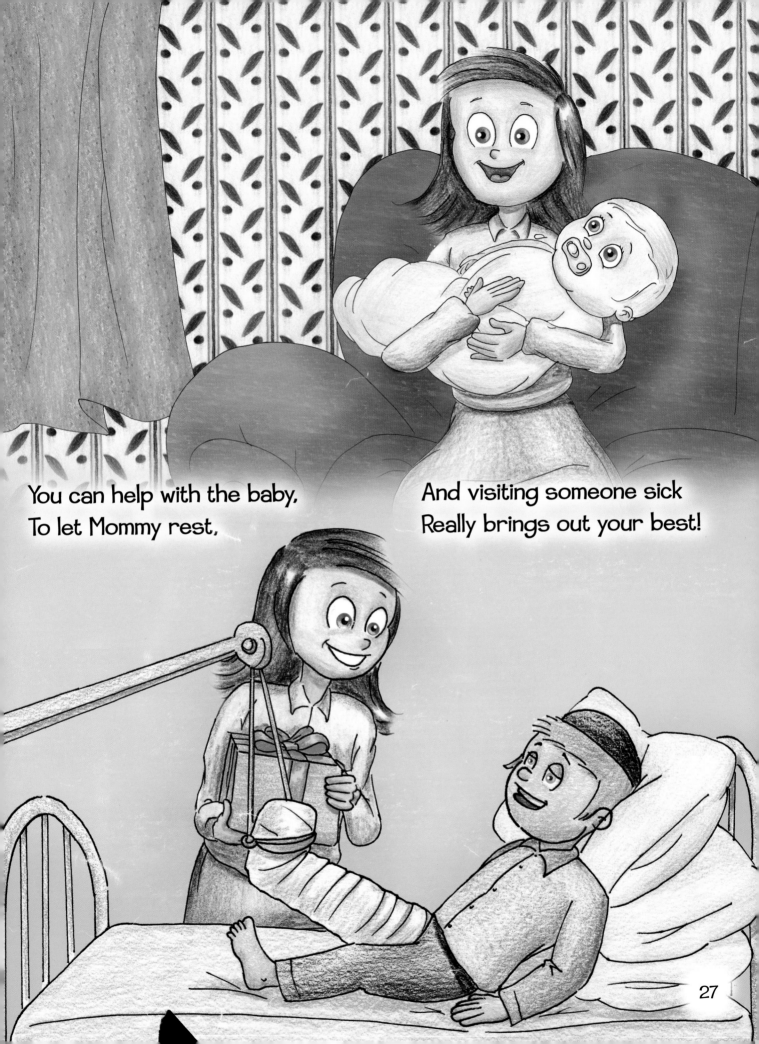

You can help with the baby,
To let Mommy rest,

And visiting someone sick
Really brings out your best!

27

You can help in the garden.
You can clean sticky walls!

28

You can make cheery cards
And friendly phone calls!

In the mirror, Aliza saw
There's so much you can do
To let others know
They're important to you.

So the next time you're bored,
Lend someone a hand!
Look for ways to help others,
And you'll find MitzvahLand!

30